The Myst

What Happened to the Bishop

n 1535, Henry VIII headed to Winchester with his eyes set one very special prize; a mysterious golden tankard which was ocked in the vaults of the cathedral. According to local legend, this tankard held mystical power, which guaranteed the owner a continuous flow of gold for the duration of their lifetime. So secretive and valuable was this tankard, that few had ever seen it, and its very appearance was shrouded in mystery.

Deep in debt, Henry hatched a plan to seize the magical tankard and store it in his London treasury, in a desperate attempt to reverse his failing economic fortunes.

As guests gathered for a lavish ceremony, the Bishop of Winchester cracked open the antique box for the excited king, who was stunned to see that the golden tankard had been stolen!

Who would take such a risk and steal from the King of England? Was it an opportunist thief? Or was it part of a deeper plot? You must solve the clues to eliminate suspects, discover the appearance of the tankard, & finally unravel the details of this legendary Tudor mystery!

The story detailed throughout this book is fictional, but the historical information provided with each clue is based on detailed research into true tales and folklore of local characters & events.

HOW TO PLAY

1 **Follow the Maps** to find the location of your clue

2 **Solve the Clue** to eliminate one option from the list on page 1 (Extra help is on the back page)

3 At each stop you will **Unravel more of the legendary tale.**

4 At the end of your adventure your last remaining items on Page 1 will **Reveal the final Secrets of the Mystery**

IMPORTANT INFORMATION

1 On rare occasions, clues may be temporarily covered or permanently removed. In this instance we ask you to use the extra clues at the back the book, and if possible, please report this to us.
It is recommended that you do the activity within 3 months of purchase, to reduce this risk.

2 Take care! You are responsible for yourself and your group. Be careful crossing roads, make sure to respect old monuments and private property, and if you are drinking alcohol please drink responsibly.

3 Any food & drink discounts available in this booklet are at the discretio of the stated premises, and may be subject to change or cancellation.

DIRECTIONS TO STARTING POINT

THE STARTING POINT FOR THIS ADVENTURE IS:

WINCHESTER PLAGUE MEMORIAL (MONUMENT)
UPPER HIGH STREET, SO23 8UT

ONCE ARRIVING AT THE STARTING POINT,
YOUR MYSTERY ADVENTURE CAN BEGIN!

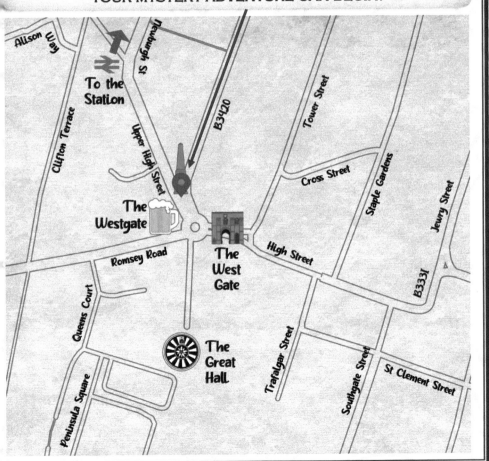

Clue 1

0	1	2	3	4	5	6	7	8	9
W	G	T	O	R	T	S	A	N	E

Find a date, set in stone,
when the **ninetieth feast** occurred.
Translate each digit, to a letter,
to spell out two four-letter words:

23   08   17 5 9

DD MM YYYY

ELIMINATE   *Eliminate a meeting place*

TOWN GATE

Just to this south of this spot is the Great Hall, which in 1522 was the venue for a momentous meeting between Henry VIII and King Charles V of Spain, who agreed a secret alliance against the French in exchange for the betrothal of Henry's daughter Mary to the Spanish king. During the meeting Henry showed off his famous 'Round Table', claiming it had once belonged to the legendary King Arthur and his knights, although modern technology actually dates it to the 13th century, meaning the legend of this Arthurian relic was purely a Tudor myth. Due to the outbreak of plague in London in 1603, the Great Hall was chosen as the venue for the blockbuster trial of Sir Walter Raleigh, who was sentenced to beheading for plotting against England in secret negotiations with Spain.

STORY..

On the evening of 18th September 1535 Henry VIII arrived in Winchester to survey his kingdom and introduce his subjects to their new queen, Anne Boleyn. A lavish banquet was prepared, with a string of VIP guests in attendance. As festivities dragged on Henry grew impatient to make a toast from the legendary golden tankard and called for the bishop to "bring it forth at once". Unfortunately for Henry the bishop had already left to deal with some secret business...

Directions

Head south from the monument, turn left at the roundabout, and walk through the old stone gate. Continue along the High Street and follow the road as it bends to the left of a pedestrianised street. Your next clue is somewhere in the area outlined on the map by a dotted line.

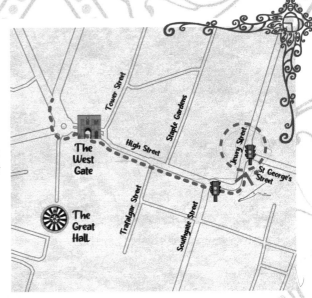

The Westgate

Clue 2

Hunt for your next clue within the dotted line outlined on the map on the previous page.

> The next piece of this Tudor puzzle lies somewhere in this zone, seeds of suspicion have been planted, and carved out to you in stone.

Eliminate a **tankard emblem**

ELIMINATE

You just passed through the 11th century Westgate, which during the Tudor period was used as a debtors' prison. Intricate graffiti which inmates carved into the stone walls can still be seen today. While conditions on the ground floor could be dire; the upper chamber was reserved for more 'respectable gentlemen' who were imprisoned in relative comfort... so much so that many preferred time in jail to the prospect of repaying large debts, leading one infuriated creditor to label the prison "a haven for the spendthrift". Westgate's most famous inmate was King Charles I who was briefly detained here en-route to his fateful trial in London. When the Mayor followed tradition and presented Charles with the city's keys, he was attacked by an angry mob.

STORY..

THE LEGEND THE GOLDEN TANKARD AND ITS WEALTH-GIVING POWERS BEGAN UNDER THE SAXON KING ATHELSTAN. HE WAS THE RICHEST MAN IN THE KINGDOM, AND CLAIMED HIS FORTUNE CAME POURING IN AFTER DRINKING FROM A MAGICAL GOLDEN CUP. SUCH STORIES EVENTUALLY CAUGHT THE EAR OF HENRY'S CHANCELLOR, THOMAS CROMWELL, WHO SAW IT AS THE PERFECT GIFT FOR A KING WHO WAS BANKRUPT DUE TO WAR.

Directions

From the site of the clue, turn back and cross the road at the traffic lights, and then turn left into St George's Street. Shortly after you will see the Royal Oak pub on your right hand side.

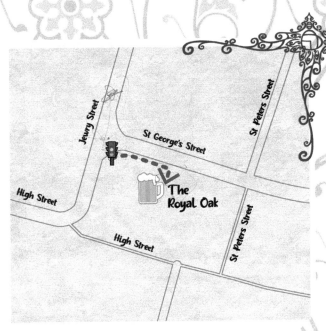

The Royal Oak

Find the 'God Begot House' sign in the alleyway running alongside the pub called 'Royal Oak Passage'.

GOD BEGOT HOUSE

526	955
776	970

Look at the top two rows of dates and see that they have been changed.

Crack the code and then apply it to the number below:

1053

2 ~~8~~ 06

Eliminate a **meeting time**

ELIMINATE

1052 1810
1522 194

Built on the remains of the former palace of Viking Queen Emma the lower walls of the Royal Oak date back to 1002 and is one o many pubs which claim to be the oldest in the country. Othe contenders include 'The Old Ferry Boat Inn' in Holywell, which believed to have been serving beer since 560, and 'The Roya Standard' in Buckinghamshire, which was detailed as an ale hous in the Domesday Book of 1086. The Royal Oak's name dates bac to the years following the English Civil War, when it was a popula gathering spot for Royalists who would wear an oak leaf to show their secret support for the exiled future king Charles II, wh famously hid from Parliamentary forces in an old oak tree befor escaping to France.

STORY..

SHORTLY BEFORE HENRY'S VISIT, WINCHESTER HAD ORDAINED THEIR NEWEST BISHOP; A LOCAL MAN BY THE NAME OF BENJAMIN WOOD. AS BISHOP, WOOD WAS ALSO NOW THE 'KEEPER OF THE GOLDEN TANKARD', WHICH HAD BEEN IN THE CHURCH'S HANDS EVER SINCE KING ATHELSTAN'S DEATH. WOOD WAS NOW SOLELY RESPONSIBLE FOR MAKING SURE THAT THE PRECIOUS RELIC NEVER LEFT ITS SECURE WOODEN CHEST IN THE VAULTS OF WINCHESTER CATHEDRAL.

Directions

Exit 'Royal Oak Passage' and head straight across the High Street and into St Thomas Street. Continue straight and then join Minister Lane on your left. After the lane, turn right and continue to the end of Symonds Street where you will see 'Christ's Hospital' on the right-hand corner. Your next clue can be found here.

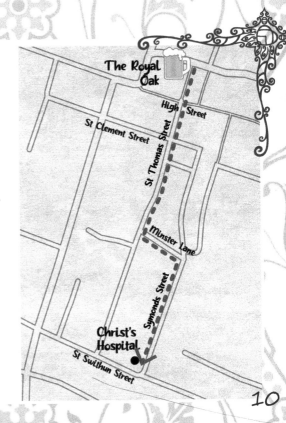

Christ's Hospital

Clue 4

Use the plaque on the wall at Christ's Hospital to complete the time below:

2   1 : 4   6

Eliminate a **meeting time**

ELIMINATE

You are now standing on the corner of St Swithun's Street, which is named after the famous 9th century Bishop of Winchester, who stated that when he died, he should be buried outside the cathedral where he would be 'subject to the feet of passers-by and to the raindrops pouring from on high'. However, 100 years after his burial, Bishop Swithun was named a Saint, and his remains were moved inside the cathedral, after which it rained for 40 consecutive days. Legend has it that the rains had been a sign of the Bishop's disapproval at being moved against his will, and ever since, it has been said that if it rains on St Swithun's Bridge on 15th July, it will continue for 40 days.

STORY..

BEFORE JOINING THE CHURCH, BENJAMIN WOOD WAS A SUCCESSFUL BUSINESSMAN, WHO SOLD HOLY CHARMS TO PILGRIMS HEADING ON TRIPS TO EUROPE. PROMISING PROTECTION FROM THE PERILS OF THE JOURNEY AHEAD, THESE CHARMS BECAME SO POPULAR THAT HE BEGAN SELLING THOUSANDS OF THEM OVERSEAS. BEFORE LONG HE'D AMASSED A SMALL FORTUNE AND QUICKLY CAUGHT THE EYE OF THE CHURCH.

Directions

Turn back the way you came along Symonds Street, and then turn right into Great Minster Street. In front of you is the entrance to the Cathedral grounds (between the stone bollards), which is the location of your next clue.

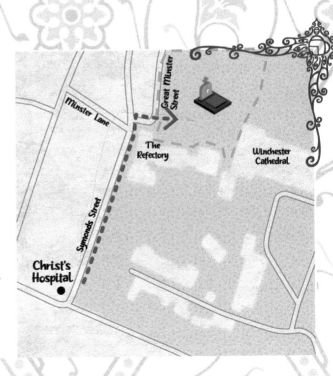

12

Clue 5

Here lies a soldier named Thomas Thetcher,
he was not stabbed or shot.
Find how he caught a violent fever,
to rule out a meeting spot.

Eliminate a **meeting place**

Winchester Cathedral is the final resting place of no fewer tha
twelve English Kings and also famed author Jane Austen, who wa
buried in 1817 at the age of just 41; an untimely end whic
many now believe was the result of arsenic poisoning. Throughou
the centuries the Cathedral has also witnessed more joyou
occasions... none bigger than in 1554, when an influx of foreig
dignitaries flocked to the city to attend the marriage of Mary
and the catholic king Philip II of Spain, who wed in Winchester fo
fear of unrest by disgruntled Protestants in London. While th
union was of great strategic importance, it was perhaps not th
best physical match for Philip, with one of his courtiers describin
the royal bride as, "old, badly dressed and almost toothless."

STORY..

WHILE MANY WERE HAPPY THAT A LOCAL WINCHESTER RESIDENT HAD GOT TO THE POSITION OF BISHOP, WOOD WAS SEEN BY SOME AS A MAN OF 'LOW BIRTH', HUNGRY FOR WEALTH AND POWER, AND NOT TO BE TRUSTED. SOME EVEN QUESTIONED HIS 'MORAL PURITY' DUE TO HIS FRIENDSHIP WITH A LOCAL BREWER BY THE NAME OF MATTHEW TANNER; WITH RUMOURS CIRCULATING THAT THE PAIR HAD REGULARLY INDULGED IN HEAVY DRINKING, GAMBLING AND WOMANISING DURING THEIR YOUTH.

Directions

Walk towards the main doors to the cathedral, and then follow it round to the right and though a stone archway. Continue walking along the side of the cathedral to the end, and then turn right.

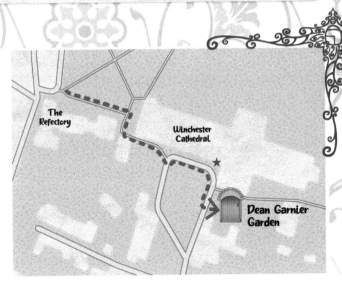

On your left you will see a line of old stone pillars with an old wooden door to the right. The wooden door is the entrance to Dean Garnier Garden, which is the location for your next clue.
If the door is locked, an alternative clue can be found on the back page of this booklet, and is marked on the map with a ★

Dean Garnier Garden

Clue 6

Your next clue can be found within Dean Garnier Garden. If the door is locked, go to the back page for an alternative clue.

Find Thomas Garnier, all in black, hiding on his land. And eliminate the item he is holding in his hand.

Eliminate a tankard emblem

ELIMINATE

Following his famous break with Catholic Rome, Henry VIII ordered a valuation of all church property in his kingdom to discover how much wealth he now owned as head of the Church of England. In the years that followed, monasteries throughout the land were plundered for anything of value, from gold plates, church bells and even the lead from their roofs. St Swithun's Priory, which had stood on this spot since the 7th century, sadly did not escape his grasp, and the site was completely ransacked before being dissolved completely in 1539. Henry made the modern-day equivalent of billions of pounds from his dissolution of the monasteries... however squandered most of it on wars with France.

STORY..

SOME SAY THAT BENJAMIN WOOD WAS ONLY APPOINTED BISHOP AFTER PAYING A HUGE BRIBE TO HENRY VIII'S CHANCELLOR, THOMAS CROMWELL. HOW ELSE COULD IT BE THAT AN UNKNOWN CLERGYMAN WAS SUDDENLY PROMOTED TO THE MOST LUCRATIVE POSITION IN THE COUNTRY, WITHOUT SOME SORT OF SINISTER PLOT AT PLAY? AFTER ALL, CROMWELL HIMSELF HAD CLIMBED THE RANKS OF GOVERNMENT FROM NOWHERE, AND WAS RUMOURED TO BE 'EASILY SEDUCED BY THE LURES OF GOLD'.

Directions

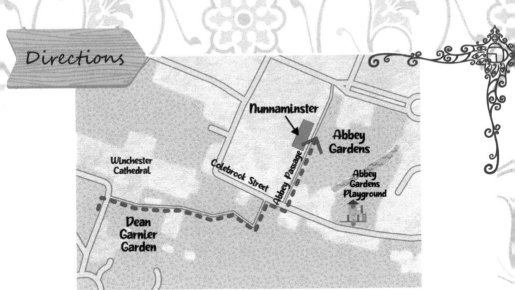

Exit the garden from the old wooden door and turn right, then right again into an old stone archway. Follow the wall-lined path all the way until you emerge onto Colebrook Street, then turn right. Take a quick left into an alley that runs alongside the carpark (marked by a bollard), and follow the path until you reach some old ruins on your left-hand side.

Nunnaminster

Clue 7

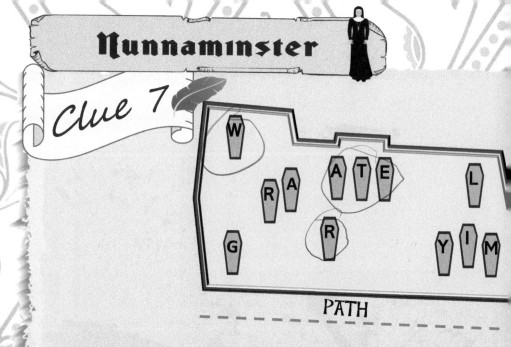

PATH

FIND 5 STONE COFFINS AMONGST THE RUINS,
AND MATCH THEIR POSITIONS TO A LETTER.
THIS 5-LETTER WORD, LINKS YOU TO A SUSPECT
TO RULE OUT FROM THE CRIME ALTOGETHER.

Eliminate a suspect

Here lies the remains of St. Mary's Abbey, or 'Nunnaminster' which was founded in 903 and served as a Benedictine Monastery. At a time when monasteries were often the only places to house libraries, this site was famed throughout the land as being the country's foremost centre of knowledge, education and art. Tragically, in 1539 the abbey suffered the same fate as St. Swithun's Priory, when it was plundered for its riches and dissolved by Henry VIII, before later being gifted back to the city by Mary I to cover the cost of her extravagant wedding to Philip.

STORY..

ONE LOCAL RESIDENT WHO WASN'T CELEBRATING THE ARRIVAL OF HENRY WAS THE NIECE OF THE FORMER BISHOP OF WINCHESTER. HENRY HAD DEPOSED HER UNCLE DUE TO HIS CATHOLIC BELIEFS; CONFISCATING HIS WEALTH AND LEAVING THEIR FAMILY IMPOVERISHED. SHE CONTINUED TO BE A REGULAR VISITOR TO THE CATHEDRAL, AND ALWAYS VOWED TO GET HER REVENGE AGAINST THE KING...

Directions

Continue down the path and you will emerge at The Broadway. Turn left, and after a few paces you will see Winchester's Guildhall on your left-hand side, which is the location of your next clue.

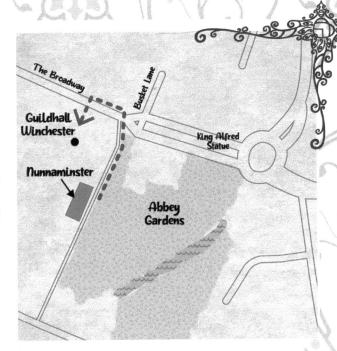

The Guildhall

Clue 8

Use the information on the outside wall of the Guildhall to solve the clue below...

54

20   GREENWICH   24

21 : 04 : 08

of

5 8

WHAT TIME IS IT IN WINCHESTER?

Eliminate a **meeting time**

ELIMINATE

In the 11th century, Winchester was home to the ruling government and site of the Royal Treasury, which made it a top priority for William the Conqueror to take after his success in the Battle of Hastings. After his arrival he quickly ordered the construction of a new Royal Palace and Cathedral to display his wealth and power, and also ordered a 'Great Survey' to calculate potential taxes he could raise, and the number of able men he could use to fill his army. The vast survey took over 2 years to complete and all information was sent to Winchester to be compiled into 'The Winchester Book', later known as 'The Domesday Book', which William never got to hold, as he died a year before its completion.

STORY..

ANOTHER LOCAL RESIDENT KEEN TO KEEP THE GOLDEN TANKARD AWAY FROM THE KING WAS WINCHESTER'S MAYOR, DUDLEY MANNERS. FEARING FOR THE CITY'S FINANCIAL FUTURE SHOULD THE MAGICAL RELIC BE REMOVED, MANNERS MADE CROMWELL A DESPERATE OFFER: HENRY WOULD BECOME THE OWNER OF THE TANKARD, BUT IT WOULD REMAIN UNDER PROTECTION IN WINCHESTER CATHEDRAL. HIS OFFER WAS REFUSED AND, WHEN THE TANKARD WENT MISSING, MANNERS WAS IMMEDIATELY ARRESTED AS A PRIME SUSPECT.

Directions

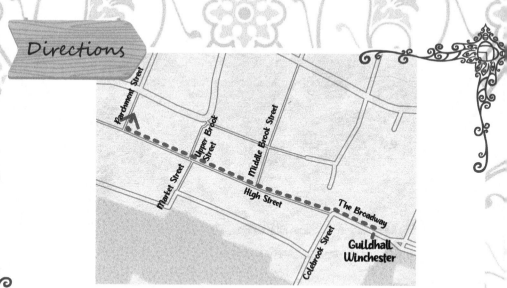

Continue along The Broadway and into the pedestrianised High Street, and after around 300m you will see Parchment Street on your right. As you enter this street, you will see five old shields above the curved bay windows on your left, which you will need to decipher your next clue.

Parchment Street

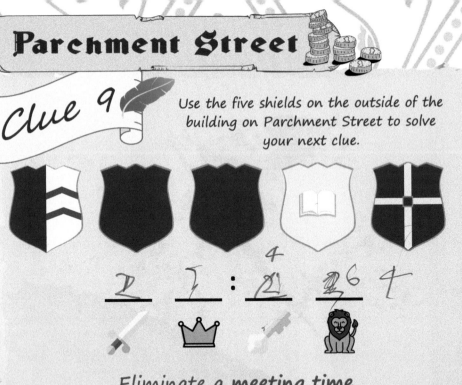

Clue 9

Use the five shields on the outside of the building on Parchment Street to solve your next clue.

Eliminate a meeting time

ELIMINATE

Located just outside William the Conqueror's Royal Palace, this area was the original site of the Winchester Mint, and it is estimated that between the 9th to 13th centuries at least 24 million silver pennies were minted here. Workers at the mint had to be fairly wealthy, educated and trustworthy enough to be granted such a significant job, and should they be caught issuing light or debased coins they would suffer the gruesome fate of having their hand cut off. Interestingly the largest collection of Winchester pennies is now housed in St Petersburg, as they were used to pay annual protection money to Vikings, and eventually made their way into circulation in Russia.

STORY..

When Henry VIII split from the Catholic church, it had a catastrophic effect on Benjamin Wood's charm business. Banned from exporting to Europe, his fortunes collapsed overnight. To make matters worse, Wood now owed a large debt to Thomas Cromwell after agreeing a secret bribe to secure his position as Bishop. It was a debt Cromwell was expecting to be paid in full before he returned to London...

Directions

Re-join the High Street and continue straight until you see a large stone monument on your left. Head through the covered alleyway just to the right of it (next to the pasty shop) which is an area that once formed part of William the Conqueror's Royal Palace. As you emerge from the small street of cafes, you will see the City Museum on your left, with an old Tudor building opposite called The Eclipse pub, which is your next stopping point.

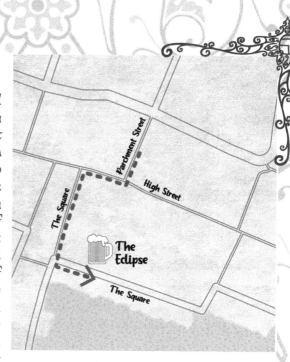

The Eclipse

Clue 10

Find this plaque opposite the pub:

Place the missing words in order, to complete the sentence below:

This___ Building___

is ___on the site___

where a___ group of___

citizens___

sing___ or ___Act___

Eliminate a meeting place

ELIMINATE

XXXX XXXXXXXX stands on XXX XXXX of the Old Cornmarket and combined the structures of two houses to form The Winchester Provident Dispensary, set up in 1875 by X XXXXX XX local XXXXXXXX to provide medical help for the families of insured people before the pasXXXX of the National Health XXX in 1949.

Dating back to 1540, this stunning Tudor building was the site of arguably the most shocking moment in this city's history. Following defeat at the Battle of Sedgemoor, two fleeing soldiers were offered refuge in the house of Alice Lisle, but their cover was blown the next morning and they were all arrested. Wishing to make an example of Miss Lisle for harbouring traitors, the famous Judge Jeffries' sentenced her to death by burning, but her sentence was changed to beheading after an intervention of mercy from King James II. Alice spent her last night in this very building before climbing out of the top window and onto the scaffolding outside to face the executioner's axe; becoming the last woman in England to be publicly beheaded at the age of 68.

STORY..

Faced with the threat of bankruptcy and literally losing his head if he couldn't pay Cromwell's bribe, Wood was getting desperate. As part of their secret deal Cromwell had set the payment date as the night of the presentation ceremony, and was expecting him to deliver a large bag of gold coins to the kitchen of Winchester's Great Hall under the cover of darkness.

Directions

Continue along the street to the end, take a right into the cathedral grounds, and then a quick left along a narrow stone path, which will put you in front of the black railings of Morley College.

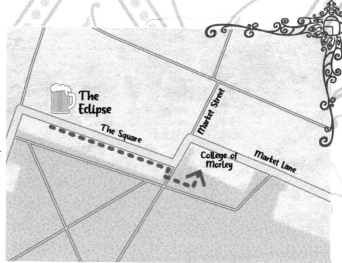

Morley College

Find this plaque at Morley College, and use the missing letters to spell out a six-letter word below:

G L O U E S

Eliminate a tankard emblem

ELIMINATE

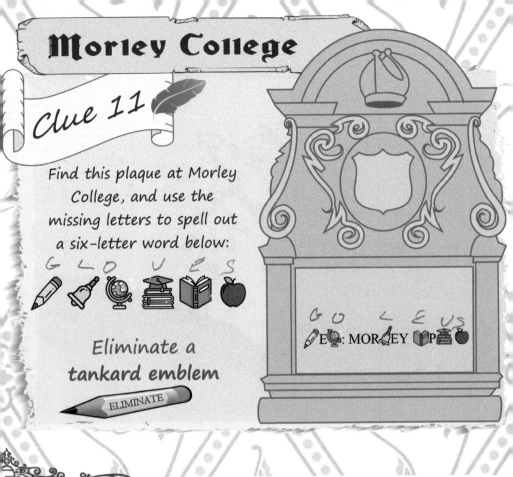

G O L E U S

E : MORLEY P

By the early 1900s the cathedral was in a bad state of repair with huge cracks appearing in the walls that were large enough for owls to roost in. The building desperately needed to be underpinned, however every time they attempted to dig trenches they immediately filled with water. A radical solution was eventually proposed; to hire a diver to go under the water and lay thousands of bags of cement by hand. The call was answered by William Walker, a deep-sea diver from Portsmouth's dockyard who after 6 years of back-breaking labour submerged under muddy water, saved the building from collapse. For his efforts Walker was presented with the Royal Victorian Order and a statue of him in his diving suit stands proudly at the cathedral.

Story..

As Wood ran out of options, he turned to his old friend Matthew Tanner, who was the rich owner of a local brewery. Maybe he would lend him the bribe money? The problem was, Tanner was a secret Catholic and he would never agree to give money to Cromwell. How could they hatch a plan to pay off Cromwell and keep the city's iconic golden tankard away from Henry? ..

Directions

Follow the paths across the grass to the main door of the cathedral, and as you did last time, head through the stone archway to the right. You will immediately see your next clue.

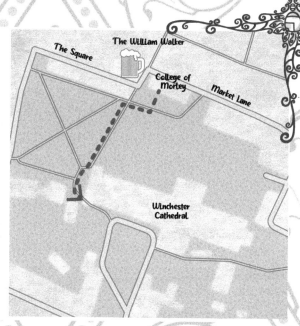

The Square

The William Walker

College of Morley

Market Lane

Winchester Cathedral

26

Winchester Cathedral

Clue 12

Find this inscription on the wall of the cathedral:

HIS , DECEM
ADMINICVLIS
SVFFVLTA EST
ECCLESIA
? ? ? ? ? ? ?

Translation:
'With these ten supports the church is held up'.

Use the missing letters to complete the sentence:

Rich local merchant m _a_ _d_ e M_u_C_h_ m_i_X_l_ng v_l_nes.

Eliminate a tankard emblem

Construction of Winchester Cathedral began in 1079 on the site of the original 7th century Saxon church known as the 'Old Minster', whose footprint can still be seen marked out in brick on the cathedral lawn. When Winchester fell to Parliamentary forces during the Civil War, drunken troops rampaged through the city, eventually reaching the cathedral where they broke open the tombs of Anglo-Saxon saints and decided to throw their bones through the priceless stained-glass windows. When Charles II came to the throne, attempts were made to piece together the original shards of glass and reconstruct the windows exactly as they had been, but the task proved impossible. It was therefore decided to melt the fragments into the mosaic pattern that can be seen above the main entrance to this day.

STORY..

AS WORD OF THE BISHOP'S DESPERATION SPREAD, CHURCH OFFICIALS BECAME INCREASINGLY CONCERNED FOR THE WELFARE OF THE GOLDEN TANKARD. A PLAN WAS HATCHED FOR SENIOR PRIEST, HOWARD GRAY, TO ENTER THE CATHEDRAL AT NIGHT AND CHECK THAT IT WAS STILL SAFE INSIDE ITS BOX. THAT NIGHT HOWEVER, BISHOP WOOD RETURNED UNEXPECTEDLY, AND CAUGHT HIM IN THE VAULT. WHEN THE TANKARD WAS FOUND TO BE MISSING THE FOLLOWING DAY, GRAY WAS ADDED TO THE LIST OF KEY SUSPECTS.

Directions

This time as you emerge from the passageway, follow the road round to the right, and as you come to a junction, turn left towards an old timber-framed building. Keeping that old building on your left, continue straight, until you see an old gate in the corner. Head through the gate and turn left through another gateway, continuing straight until you see the Wykeham Arms pub on the corner.

The Wykeham Arms

Clue 13

Search for the motto of the pub,
to solve this if you can:
The answer to the simple question:
What is it that makes a man?

Eliminate a **suspect**

ELIMINATE

Take a photo

Tag on social media: @mysteryguides

PHOTO STOP!

For a chance to win a prize!!

This pub is named after one of Winchester's most celebrated residents, William Wykeham, who from humble beginnings rose to become Lord Chancellor to King Richard II and founder of Winchester College. As a boy, William relied on the generosity of wealthy local patrons to gain a place at a school in Winchester, but went on to accumulate a vast personal fortune through his work as a skilled architect, and eventually held the title of 'Bishop of Winchester'; the richest position in the land. Legend has it that this pub once hosted none other than Lord Horatio Nelson as he stopped for the night on his way to Portsmouth. You will notice that many of the pub's tables are old school desks acquired from the nearby college.

STORY..

TRUE TO HIS WORD, WHEN THE TIME WAS RIGHT BISHOP WOOD MET THE WAITING CROMWELL IN THE KITCHEN OF THE GREAT HALL, AND HANDED HIM A BAG OF SHINY GOLD COINS... BUT HOW DID HE GET SUCH AN INCREDIBLE SUM AT SHORT NOTICE? THE ANSWER MAY LIE IN WHAT HE DID NEXT... WOOD ENTERED THE CATHEDRAL IN THE DEAD OF NIGHT TO REMOVE THE GOLDEN TANKARD, WHICH HE PLANNED TO GIVE TO A MYSTERIOUS FIGURE WAITING NEARBY...

Directions

As you exit the Wykeham Arms, head back the way you came, but take a right into College Street. Continue for around 150 metres, (passing the house that Jane Austen died in) until you see the entrance to Winchester College on your right (beneath the statue of a female holding a baby).

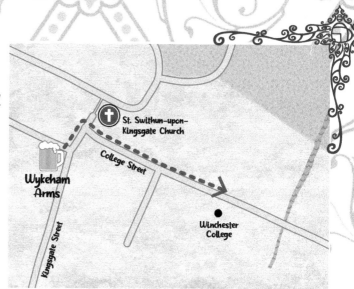

Winchester College

1597

Clue 14

Find this badge on the outside of the college:
You will find two gold letters

L H
H G

Oliver Twist

BF   **DE**   **XT**

A E   *C D*   *W S*

Work out the code, then apply it to your two letters.

Eliminate a **suspect**

ELIMINATE

Winchester College has the longest continuous history of any school in England, with an impressive list of former pupils known as 'Wykehamists' who often fill the country's most powerful political positions alongside their rival 'Etonians'. During the Tudor period, the college had a particularly controversial headmaster by the name of John White, whose staunch Catholic beliefs led to a rather turbulent life. Imprisoned in the Tower of London by the protestant king Edward VI, he was later released and promoted to become the Bishop of Winchester under catholic Mary I. It was during this time that White became the enforcer of 'Bloody Mary's' strict religious persecutions, arranging the public burnings of a host of high-profile protestants. He was eventually sent back to the Tower when Elizabeth I came to the throne, and died shortly after.

STORY..

THE NEXT MORNING, GUESTS GATHERED IN WINCHESTER CATHEDRAL TO WITNESS HENRY FINALLY BEING PRESENTED WITH THE MAGICAL GOLDEN TANKARD. AS BISHOP WOOD TOOK THE KEY FROM AROUND HIS NECK AND SLOWLY OPENED THE WOODEN TOP, SHOCKED GASPS ECHOED AROUND THE CATHEDRAL AT THE SIGHT OF AN EMPTY CHEST. A HUMILIATED HENRY ANGRILY ORDERED THE CITY GATES BE LOCKED AND COMMANDED CROMWELL TO HUNT DOWN THE TANKARD IMMEDIATELY...

Directions

Continue along College Street, and as the road ends, head left along the walking track which runs beside the remains of Wolvesey castle. Your next clue can be found close to a cut-down tree.

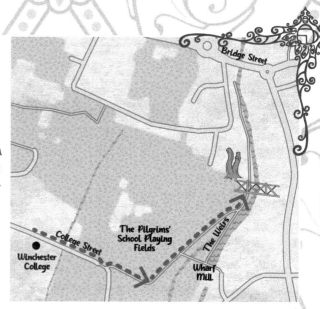

The River Itchen

During the middle ages the Bishop of Winchester was a powerful landlord, with control over large swathes of land both within Winchester and beyond. One such area was the borough of Southwark in London, whose location just outside of the jurisdiction of the city made it a popular gathering spot for prostitutes. Rather than condemning these working girls, the Bishop gave them a special licence to work in the borough in return for a tax on their income. This created a rowdy and competitive environment and the streets were filled with the deafening sound of screeching girls vying for trade, gaining them the nickname 'Winchester Geese'. In Tudor times, a common euphemism for catching syphilis was to be 'bitten by a Winchester goose', which some say led to the modern-day expression 'to get goose bumps'.

Clue 15

YOUR CLUE'S BESIDE A WOODEN BRIDGE,
BELOW A CUT-DOWN TREE.
A VERY SPECIAL MAN NAMED **TED**,
IS WAITING THERE FOR THEE.

Eliminate the suspect whose
symbol links to Ted.

32

STORY..

As each subject was ruled out and the trail ran cold, suspicions soon turned to Cromwell himself. How could such a daring heist possibly take place without involvement from those at the top? Eagle-eyed guests at the Great Hall had noticed Cromwell was absent for long periods throughout the evening. One servant even witnessed him placing a large bag of coins onto a waiting carriage...

Directions

Continue along the walking track for a short distance, and look for the remains of the old Roman walls.

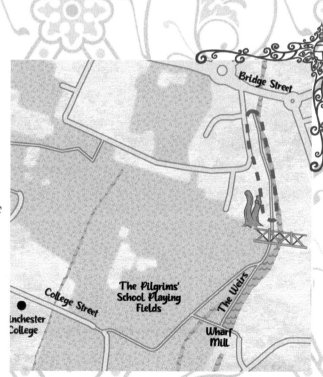

Roman Walls

Clue 16

Locate the ruins of the old Roman walls

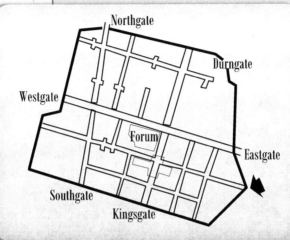

Northgate

Durngate

Westgate

Forum

Eastgate

Southgate

Kingsgate

What is missing from the plan?

Eliminate a **meeting place**

ELIMINATE

Before the Romans arrived in AD70, the area was a key trading location of the local 'Belgae' tribe, who originated from the area o Europe that we now call Belgium. Like Winchester, many of the country's important towns and cities we have today end with the word 'chester', which evolved from the Latin word 'castra' meaning 'military camp'. Part of this area's original name 'Venta was merged with 'castra' to become the town we now cal 'Winchester'. As well as place names, many of the modern-day roads we use today were built on original Roman paved streets including the famous Watling Street, which now forms part of the A5 and is thought to be the place where Boudica was defeated by the Romans.

STORY..

ON THAT FATEFUL NIGHT, BISHOP WOOD HAD ARRANGED TO MEET A MYSTERIOUS FIGURE ON THE BRIDGE AHEAD OF YOU, TO SECRETLY HAND OVER THE PRECIOUS TANKARD. HOWEVER, THEY WERE SUDDENLY STARTLED BY A NIGHT WATCHMAN, AND WOOD TOSSED THE TANKARD INTO A DITCH BY THE ROAD. THEY QUICKLY FLED THE SCENE, LEAVING THE PRICELESS RELIC LYING IN THE MUD WHERE A NEW TAVERN WAS BEING BUILT. BUT WHO DID THE BISHOP MEET ON THAT LEGENDARY NIGHT? AND WHAT WAS THE FINAL FATE OF THE MAGICAL GOLDEN TANKARD?

THE MYSTERY IS SOLVED!!!

Continue along the river and you'll **find a pub**, which lies at the centre of this Tudor mystery...

Then turn over for the final chapter..

Bridge Street

Colebrook Street

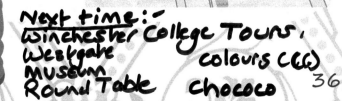

Next time:-
Winchester College Tours,
Westgate
Museum   colours (CCC)
Round Table   Chococo

36

THE FINAL CHAPTER..

THE MYSTERIOUS FIGURE WAITING ON THE BRIDGE FOR BISHOP WOOD WAS NONE OTHER THAN HIS BEST FRIEND MATTHEW TANNER, WHO HAD FINALLY AGREED TO GIVE HIM CROMWELL'S BRIBE IN EXCHANGE FOR THE GOLDEN TANKARD..

RATHER THAN DIGGING IT UP FROM THE DITCH, TANNER BUILT HIS NEW TAVERN RIGHT ON TOP OF THE TANKARD'S RESTING PLACE, WHERE LEGEND HAS IT, IT LIES HIDDEN TO THIS DAY.

AS A CLUE TO HIS INVOLVEMENT, TANNER NAMED THE PUB 'THE BISHOP ON THE BRIDGE' AND ADOPTED THE GOLDEN TANKARD'S FAMOUS DOUBLE HERON EMBLEM FOR THE SIGN OUTSIDE. THE TANKARD'S LEGENDARY POWER LIVED UP TO ITS NAME, AS THE TAVERN WAS A HUGE SUCCESS, MAKING HIM THE WEALTHIEST BREWER IN THE LAND.

CROMWELL'S FUTURE HOWEVER WAS NOT SO ROSY. HIS UNDERHAND DEALINGS FINALLY CAUGHT UP WITH HIM, AND HE WAS EXECUTED FOR TREASON IN 1540.

SHORTLY AFTER THE DISAPPEARANCE OF THE GOLDEN TANKARD, BENJAMIN WOOD STEPPED DOWN FROM HIS POST AS BISHOP OF WINCHESTER AND RETURNED TO THE BUSINESS WORLD, WHERE HE FOUND SUCCESS SELLING A BRAND-NEW PRODUCT; PEWTER REPLICAS OF THE FAMOUS GOLDEN TANKARD.

Did you enjoy the Treasure Hunt?
I'd love to hear about your Adventure!

Review us on Tripadvisor

Lovely way to spend the afternoon

Scan the QR code to leave a review.. (it would make my day... thanks!) 😊

We loved it, and would highly recommend!

History, mystery and fun!